STICKER THERAPY

NATURE

FOLLOW THE NUMBERS TO COMPLETE
12 MEDITATIVE STICKER PUZZLES

Bath · New York · Cologne · Melbourne · Delhi
Hong Kong · Shenzhen · Singapore

This edition published by Parragon Books Ltd in 2017

Parragon Books Ltd
Chartist House
15–17 Trim Street
Bath BA1 1HA, UK
www.parragon.com

Puzzles created by Any Puzzle Media Ltd

ISBN 978-1-4748-6933-1

Printed in China

Images courtesy of iStock.

HOW TO...

Our natural world is a breathtaking source of beauty, wonder and pleasure. Whether it is the small, rich details, such as a dragonfly shimmering its wings in the sunshine above a woodland river or the awesome magnificence of a snow-capped range of mountains, the character of our world is defined and enriched by every natural element.

Here is a new way of enjoying the diverse range of nature — 12 natural scenes that you can create using a dizzying array of coloured stickers. The simpler images, such as the tropical unicornfish, have just under 100 stickers and the more complex ones, such as the mandrill monkey, over 250 stickers. The stickers for the 12 puzzles add up to over 2,000 in all, so you will have your work cut out (or rather stickers to peel off and attach) before you end up with a final presentation book of 12 magnificent portraits of nature.

Each black-and-white puzzle image, with each subject portrayed in its natural context, sits on the right-hand page. Every sticker shape is numbered on the puzzle so you just need to find the correct sticker on the sticker sheet and place it in the correct position. The puzzle stickers are grouped at the back, and you can tear the sticker sheets out so you can keep them close as you complete each puzzle.

In our nature selection you will have the chance to create the rich ochres, ambers and golden oranges of an autumn leaf as well as create a towering wave crashing into jagged rocks in stormy seas. You will also meet a red-eyed tree frog from the neotropical rainforests with its bulging red eyes, blue streaks and orange toes and a rainbow lorikeet, native to the rainforest, coastal bush and woodland areas of Australia, with its dazzlingly vibrant plumage.

These puzzles will challenge you, relax you and give you a massive sense of achievement. They will also allow you to create memorable images of some of the sensational natural scenes and natural life distinctive to our planet.

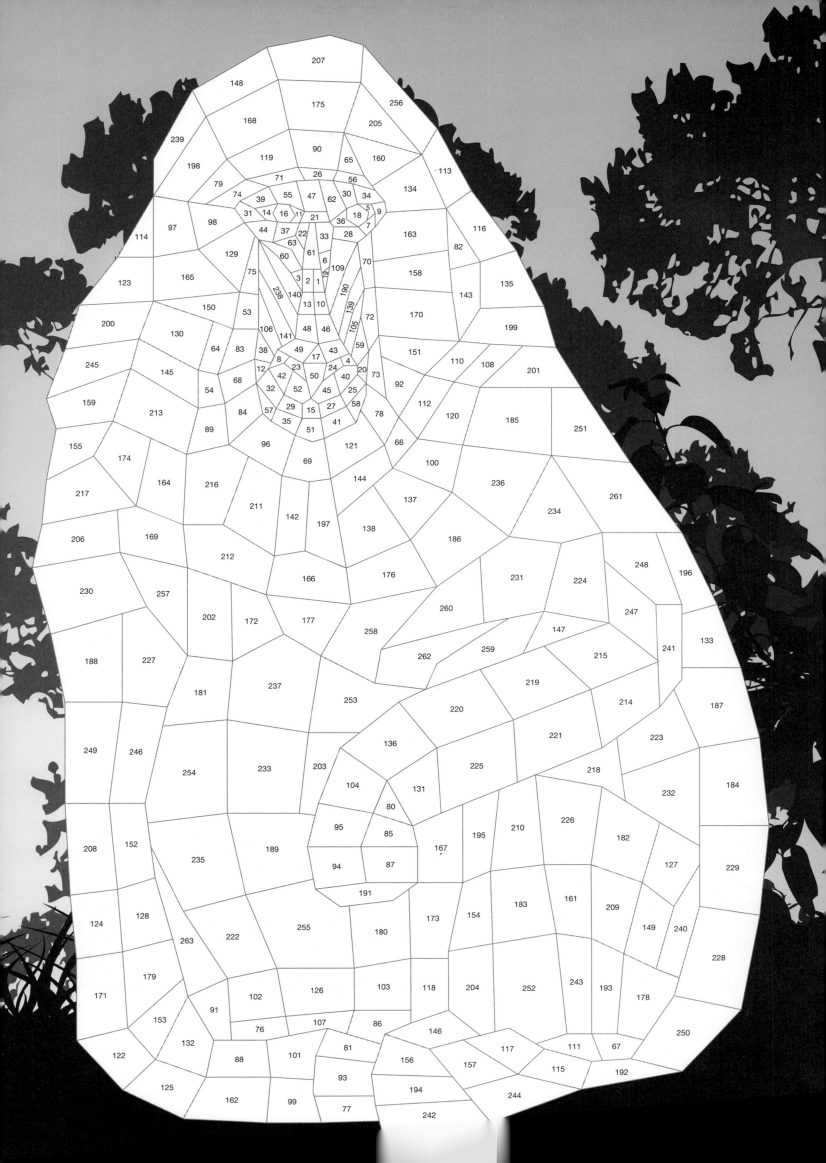